Sarah the snail has come to stay.
Connect the dots so she can play.

Keith the crab just loves to dance.
Connect the dots and watch him prance!

Connect the dots to watch Sam float around the sea on his shoe-boat!

This alien is very happy.
Connect the dots and make it snappy!

Connect the dots and you will see a queen beneath a canopy!

There's something fishy in this scene.
The fish are in a submarine!

Dave the dog likes nothing more than standing on a dinosaur.

Todd the tortoise loves his car.
Connect the dots and he'll go far!

Sydney shark slides through the snow.
Connect the dots and watch him go.

Greg the goat is no one's fool.
He understands the offside rule!

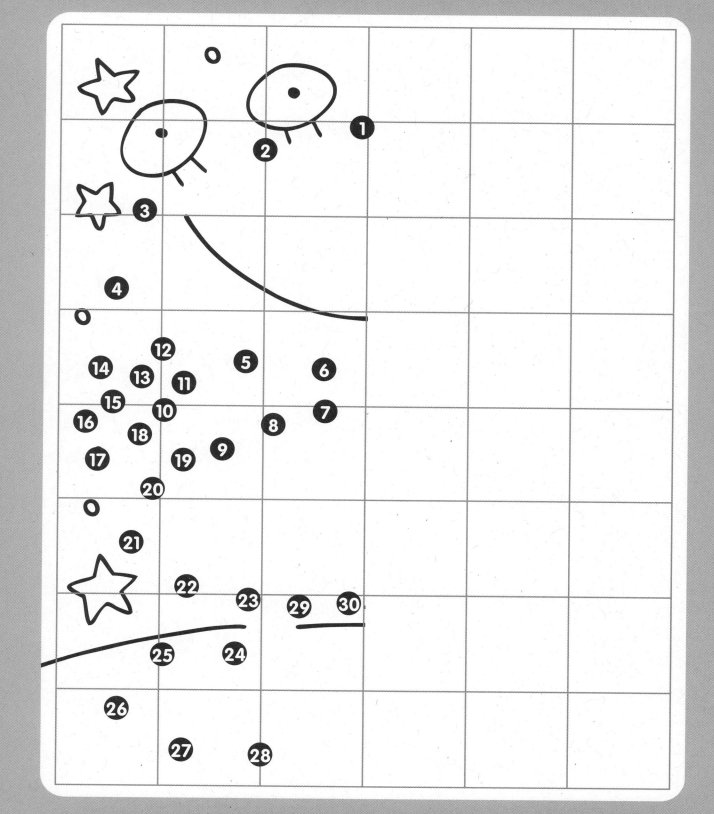

Connect the dots and then prepare
to copy the picture, square-by-square.

Connect the dots and then you can help to build this nice snowman.

Lenny the Lion loves to fish,
then cook a tasty dinner dish!

Connect the dots for Craig Cowboy, to help him ride his favourite toy.

**Connect the dots if you wish,
and you will see a snorkelling fish.**

Randolph the rabbit likes the flowers.
Connect the dots, but don't take hours!

Connect the dots and you will see
a granny swinging from a tree!

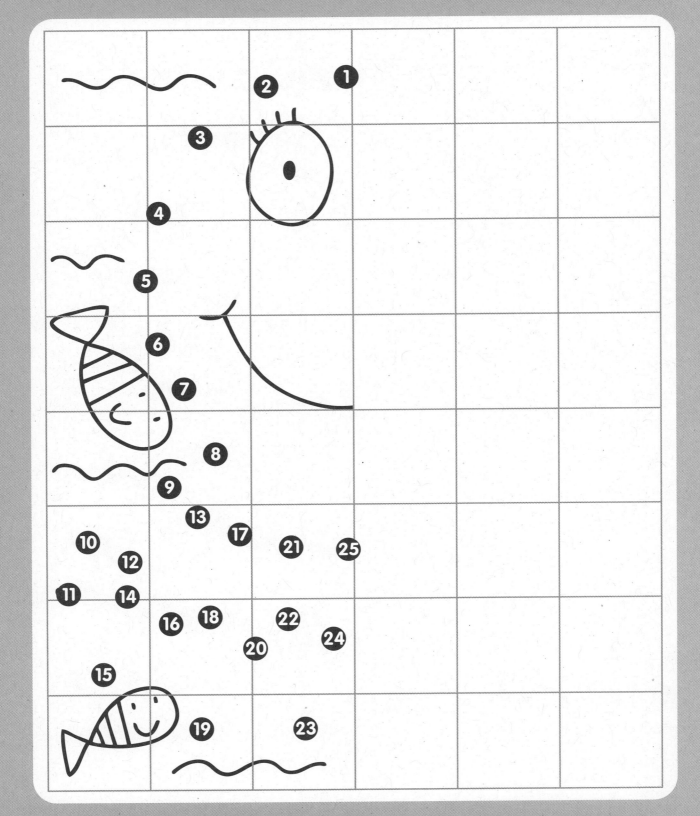

Connect the dots and then prepare to copy the picture, square-by-square.

This princess likes unusual shoes.
Connect the dots - no time to lose!

Connect the dots and you'll discover
a reindeer who's a hair-do lover!

Chris the croc is friends with fishes.
He surfs with them whenever he wishes.

**Two children rocket through the sky.
Connect the dots to help them fly.**

Sally the sheep is never glum,
when marching with her lovely drum.

When not at sea this pirate stops
to get his dinner from the shops.

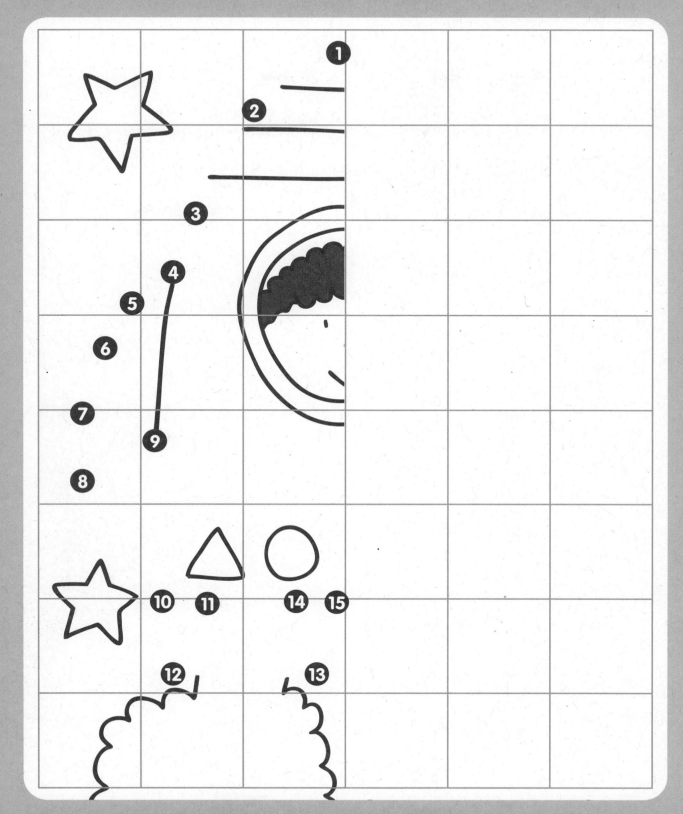

Connect the dots and then prepare to copy the picture, square-by-square.

This bee has found a tasty treat.
Connect the dots so he can eat!

Simon Star the astronaut,
says rockpooling's his favourite sport!

Connect the dots and you will spy,
a dragon strolling through the sky.

Matilda mouse is very keen
to play out on her trampoline.

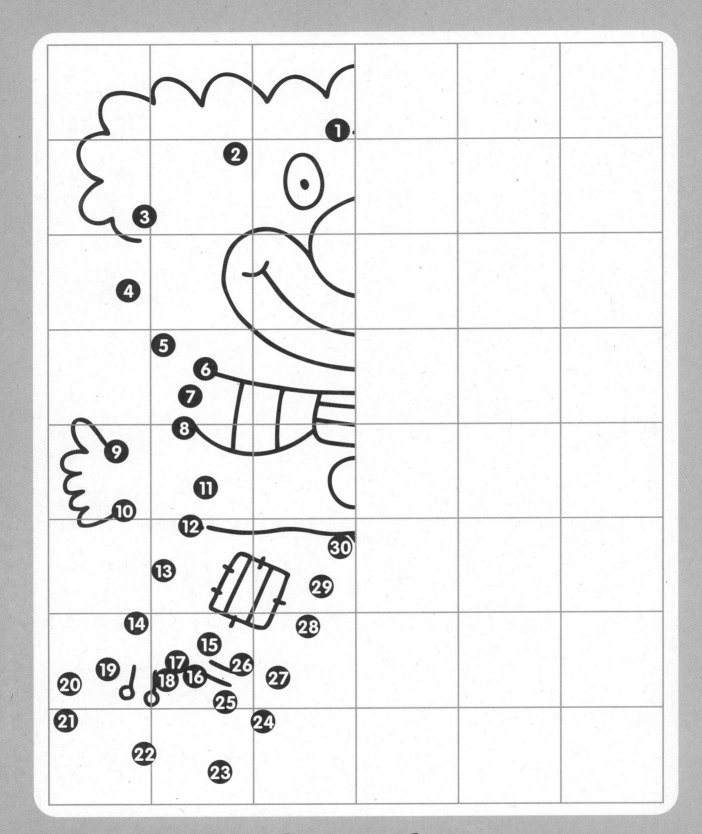

Connect the dots and then prepare
to copy the picture, square-by-square.

This funny bird is known as Clive.
He loves to go out for a drive.

Connect the dots on this android.
But quick before she gets annoyed!

Wally the wizard loves to swim.
It helps to keep his figure trim.

Terry the troll is knitting a scarf.
Connect the dots, try not to laugh.

Connect the dots, if you would like
to help this octopus ride his bike.

Helen the Hippo likes to juggle.
Connect the dots so she won't struggle.

This boy is snorkelling across the moon.
Connect the dots and do it soon!

Connect the dots and contemplate,
a young giraffe who loves to skate.

These aliens are learning to sail.
Connect the dots so they won't fail.

Swimmers make this big shark worry.
Connect the dots and watch him hurry!

Simon the snake is always skating.
Connect the dots - don't keep him waiting!

Fiona the fairy's head is bare!
Connect the dots to give her hair.

Kevin wants to have a slide.
Connect the dots to help him glide.

This young man is known as Dennis.
He likes to play his pets at tennis!

This may come as quite a shock,
but Claire the cow just loves to rock!

Fred the fisherman got a bite,
but what he caught gave him a fright!

Molly the Mermaid has a laugh,
while splashing in her bubble bath.

King Kenneth finds it rather calming, to spend his spare time doing farming.